# HOMECOMING!

WRITTEN BY

## LA-DONIA ALFORD - JEFFERIES

ILLUSTRATIONS BY

## J'AARON MERCHANT

D1452206

INGRAMSPARKS PUBLISHING

HOMECOMING!© 2019 by La-Donia Alford-Jefferies All Rights Reserved

ISBN: 978-0-578-48955-1

Cover Illustration and Formatting:
J'Aaron Merchant - @jaaronmerchant

Published in the United States of America

# Dedication

To Ivianna, Eleanor, Kingston and Emerson,

we love you fiercely.

# ABOUT

La-Donia Alford-Jefferies is a 2010 graduate of North Carolina A&T and a native to Greensboro, NC. With her mom as a former professor and her dad an alumni of the University, La-Donia was destined to become an Aggie. As an adjunct professor at the University, La-Donia is truly Aggie born and Aggie bred. Her husband, Michael, and daughters Eleanor and Emerson inspired her to write a book about their homecoming experiences as a family.

J'Aaron Merchant is a 2012 graduate of Savannah State University and a native of the U.S. Virgin Islands. As an illustrator she strives to create magical content for children of diverse backgrounds. Her mission is to provide the youth of today a window into themselves through inspiration, imagination, and illustration.

Today is finally the day! We are off on our way!
We are headed to the yard to learn the pride way!

The Greatest Homecoming is where we want to be to see our friends that are just like family.

We wear our blue and gold to the football game and cheer on our team.

The dancers move to the drums and the horns of the Marching band!

We love watching the halftime show.
The Drum major takes the lead and
her knee goes to the sky.

6

Everyone in the stadium stands up to dance to the powerful sound of the band.

After our team wins the game, it's time to eat. We head to the tailgates for a special treat.

The food smells so good!

9

We can hardly wait to eat our yummy chicken and fish plates.

Mommy and Daddy take us around the yard to see all the places they used to be at their University.

A statue of an African American Astronaut is in front of the building where Mommy took classes to become an engineer.

DR. RONALD McNAIR
October 21, 1950 – January 28, 1986
ASTRONAUT & SCIENTIST

12

We see a bulldog statue by the building where Daddy took classes to start his Veterinary business career.

We love seeing the statue of the famous four. Those brave students helped to change the world in a department store.

We head to the plots
for more fun!

Mommy and Daddy have lots of friends there. We watch as they stroll, sing songs and their voices fill the air.

They even clap their hands and stomp their feet.

My sister and I try to catch
on to the beat.

Daddy and Mommy
say its time to go, down
goes the sun.

We can't wait until next year
for more Homecoming fun!

CPSIA information can be obtained
at www.ICGtesting.com
Printed in the USA
BVHW09225615119
563900BV00001B/1/P